YELLOW STRIP

DON SHAW & JOHN SHIELS

You are the manager

_____

Your team name

_____

Colour in your kit

Home kit   **Away kit**

OXFORD UNIVERSITY PRESS

How to use this book

The purpose of this series of fill-in workbooks is to give practice in Key Stage 2 Maths in a motivating context.

The contents list shows which topic of maths is covered on each page, which maths skill this comes under, and at what level. This will give you some indication of how your child might perform in the National Tests.

First of all, your child should decide on their team name, write it in on the title page, and colour their kit in home and away colours. On each page they can decide on a different opponent, and fill in their own team in the white box and the opposing team in the tinted box. The away games are always slightly harder than the home games.

There are three kinds of page, keyed in the top corner:

    League games, which cover exercises in number and data.

    Cup games, which are all on shape and measures.

    Training sessions, which are just games for practice, and don't involve scoring.

To check your child's answers after each page, turn to the referee's decisions on page 30. Fill in your goals down the right-hand side of each page and your final score at the foot of the page. Then complete the grids below: for each league game you win, fill in 3 points, starting from the bottom of the table; for a draw, fill in just 1 point. For each cup game you win, fill in a box, starting from the bottom. If you draw 0–0, stage a replay.

 League

Champions		51 Points
Runners-up		48 Points
European place		45 Points
European place		42 Points
		39 Points
		36 Points
		33 Points
		30 Points
Mid		27 Points
Table		24 Points
		21 Points
		18 Points
		15 Points
		12 Points
Relegated		9 Points
Relegated		6 Points
Relegated		3 Points

 National Cup

	Final
	Semi-final
	Quarter-final
	4th Round
	3rd Round
	2nd Round
	1st Round

CONTENTS

An attractive first game of the season. Make home advantage count!

1 Work out how much each group pays.

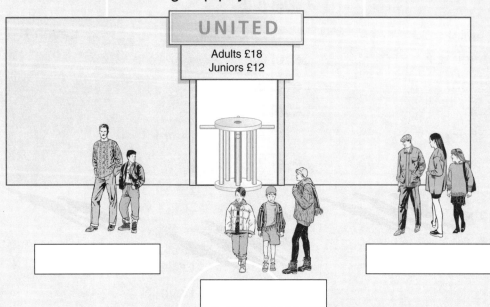

UNITED

Adults £18
Juniors £12

goal

2 Work out how much each group pays.

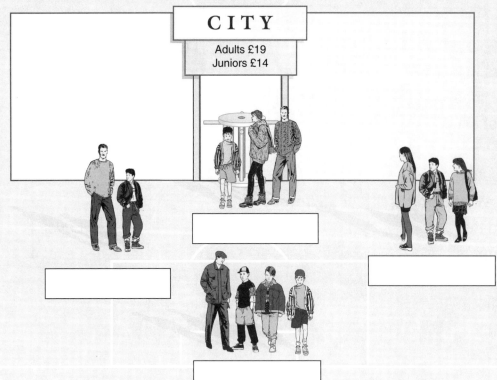

CITY

Adults £19
Juniors £14

goal

FINAL SCORE

V

1

	V	

Be patient and you can unlock their defence to score!

A	B	C	D	E	F	G	H	I	J	K	L	M	N	O	P	Q	R	S	T	U	V	W	X	Y	Z
1	5	3	5	1	4	7	5	1	8	7	2	6	3	1	4	8	3	6	2	6	7	6	8	7	8

1 Match each letter to a number, to work out how many points these teams are worth. CITY is worth 3 + 1 + 2 + 7 = 13 points

City
__13__ points

Liverpool
___ points

West Ham
___ points

Leeds
___ points

Newcastle
___ points

United
___ points

Derby
___ points

Chelsea
___ points

goal

2 Starting with the team with the most points, complete this league table.

Position	Team	Points
1		
2		
3		
4		
5		
6		
7		
8		

goal

	V	

You will get lots of chances. Concentrate in front of goal!

1 A team is awarded 3 points for a win.

1 win gives 1 × 3 points   1 × 3 = 3

2 wins give 2 × 3 points   2 × 3 = ____

3 wins give 3 × 3 points   3 × 3 = ____

4 wins give 4 × 3 points   ____ × 3 = ____

5 wins give 5 × ____ points   ____ × ____ = ____

6 wins give 6 × ____ points   ____ × ____ = ____

7 wins give ____ × ____ points   ____ × ____ = ____

8 wins give ____ × ____ points   ____ × ____ = ____

9 wins give ____ × ____ points   ____ × ____ = ____

10 wins give ____ × ____ points   ____ × ____ = ____

goal

2 Count up in 3's up to 30.

3 → ☐ → ☐ → ☐ → ☐ → ☐ → ☐ → ☐ → ☐ → 30

goal

3 Work out how many points these teams will receive for these wins.

Blackburn 6 wins ☐ points

Tottenham 3 wins ☐ points

Liverpool 7 wins ☐ points

Leeds 10 wins ☐ points

Southampton 5 wins ☐ points

Derby 2 wins ☐ points

Chelsea 4 wins ☐ points

West Ham 8 wins ☐ points

Bolton 9 wins ☐ points

goal

FINAL SCORE

	V	2

Counting in 3's join up the dots.

Then colour the picture.

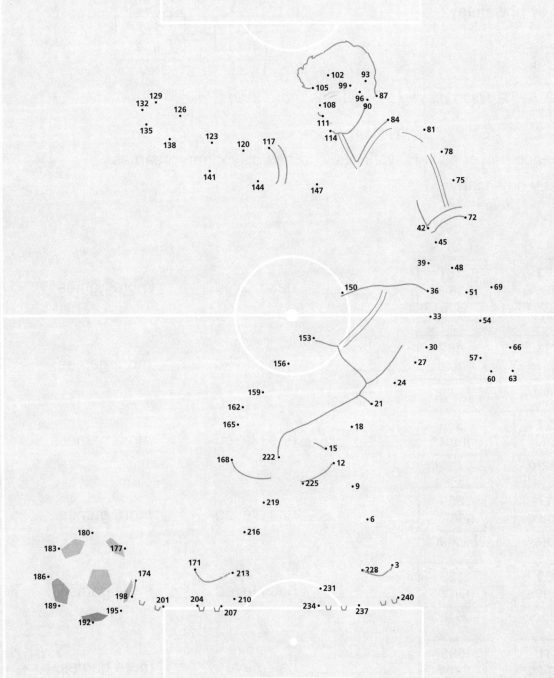

Fill in your team names

[ ] **V** [ ]

Nick a late goal and you can take away maximum points!

Who has played more games,
and by how many?

| **436** games |
| Ryan |

| **212** games |
| Steve |

```
  4 3 6
 −2 1 2
 ─────
  2 2 4
```
Ryan played 224 games more than Steve.

1 For each pair of players work out who has played more games,
and by how many.

| **373** games | **161** games |
| Dave | Pete |

_____ has played _____ more games.

| **786** games | **462** games |
| Tom | Eric |

_____ has played _____ more games.

| **127** games | **569** games |
| Adam | Daniel |

_____ has played _____ more games.

| **317** games | **659** games |
| Andrew | Richard |

_____ has played _____ more games.

| **699** games | **123** games |
| Henry | Ben |

_____ has played _____ more games.

| **241** games | **695** games |
| Jack | Sam |

_____ has played _____ more games.

goal

FINAL SCORE

[ ] **0** **V** [ ]

V

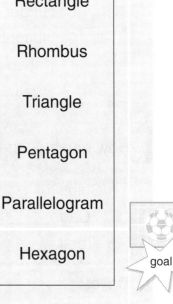

FIRST ROUND

Keep your shape at the back and you can win through!

1 Match the names to the shapes.

S _ _ _ _ _ _ _

T _ _ _ _ _ _ _

R _ _ _ _ _ _ _

C _ _ _ _ _ _ _

P _ _ _ _ _ _ _

H _ _ _ _ _ _ _

P _ _ _ _ _ _ _ _ _ _ _ _

R _ _ _ _ _ _ _

Circle
Square
Rectangle
Rhombus
Triangle
Pentagon
Parallelogram
Hexagon

goal

2 See if you can find a rhombus, a parallelogram, a hexagon and a pentagon hidden in the pictures below. Colour each a different colour.

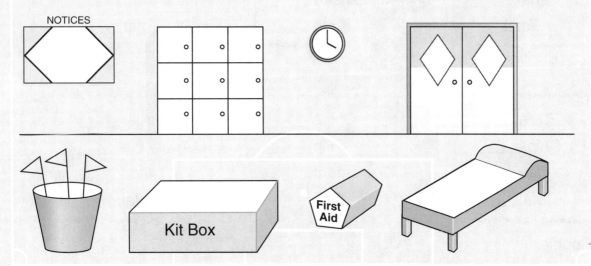

NOTICES

First Aid

Kit Box

goal

FINAL SCORE

V

0

9

	V	

You're playing well. You can add valuable points here!

City Snack Bar
Menu

Chips	...............81p	Apple pie	...........93p
Fish	...............153p	Ice cream	...........90p
Burger	............174p		
Nuggets	..........139p	Cans	................62p
Kebab	............182p		
Pizza	...............195p	Milk shake	.......134p

1 How much do these friends spend at the City Snack Bar?

Chips _____
Can _____
Total _____

Dave

Chips _____
Apple pie _____
Total _____

Steve

Nuggets _____
Milk shake _____
Total _____

Cath

Pizza _____
Milk shake _____
Total _____

Jessica

Kebab _____
Milk shake _____
Total _____

Frank

Burger _____
Ice cream _____
Total _____

John

Pizza _____
Chips _____
Can _____
Total _____

Sophie

Chips _____
Fish _____
Ice cream _____
Total _____

Vicky

Burger _____
Apple pie _____
Can _____
Total _____

Tom

goal

V

SECOND ROUND

This won't be easy. Can you measure up to the task?

Which is the most appropriate unit for measuring the following?

There may be more than one right answer to each.

Weight of ball	**Length of throw**	**Length of game**

milligrams	millimetres	seconds
grams	centimetres	minutes
kilograms	metres	hours
tonnes	kilometres	days

Weight of a blade of grass	**Length of pitch**	**Length of kick**

milligrams	millimetres	millimetres
grams	centimetres	centimetres
kilograms	metres	metres
tonnes	kilometres	kilometres

Capacity of a plastic cup	**Weight of team coach**	**Capacity of team bath**

millilitres	milligrams	millilitres
litres	grams	litres
	kilograms	
	tonnes	

goal

FINAL SCORE

0   V

Fill in your team names

[   ] **V** [   ]

Your midfield four will need to double their efforts to win!

 Each player has 4 items of kit.

1 player has 1 set of 4 items	1 × 4 = 4
2 players have 2 sets of 4 items	2 × 4 = 8
3 players have 3 sets of 4 items	3 × 4 = ____
4 players have 4 sets of 4 items	4 × 4 = ____
5 players have 5 sets of 4 items	____ × 4 = ____
6 players have 6 sets of ____ items	____ × ____ = ____
7 players have 7 sets of ____ items	____ × ____ = ____
8 players have ____ sets of ____ items	____ × ____ = ____
9 players have ____ sets of ____ items	____ × ____ = ____
10 players have ____ sets of ____ items	____ × ____ = ____

goal

 Count in 4's up to 40.

4 → 8 → [ ] → [ ] → [ ] → [ ] → [ ] → [ ] → [ ] → 40

goal

FINAL SCORE

[|] **V** [| 1]

12

V

LEAGUE

Take your chances and you're capable of getting three points!

1 Count in 4's again and fill in the gaps.

2 → 6 → ☐ → ☐ → ☐ → ☐ → ☐ → ☐ → ☐ → 38

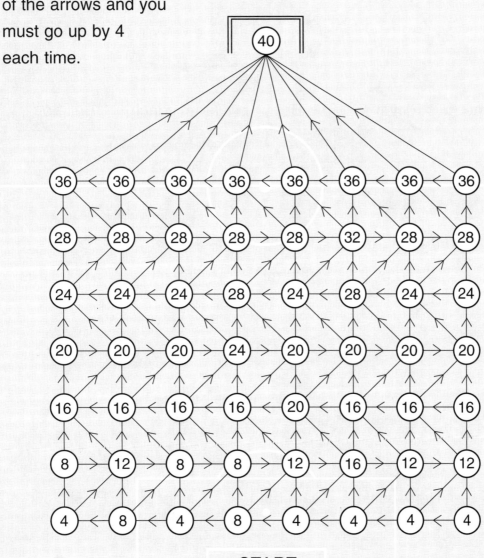

2 Find and colour a route to goal by counting up in 4's each time. You can only travel in the direction of the arrows and you must go up by 4 each time.

goal

START

goal

FINAL SCORE

1   V

13

	V	

THIRD ROUND

This should be an easy match for a team with your skill!

1 Match these weights with the objects below.

12 tonnes	30 kg	85 kg	100 g	400 g

Programme	Player	Ball	Team coach	Ball boy

goal

2 Match these capacities with the objects below.

10 litres	150 ml	300 ml	750 ml	15 000 litres

Can	Drink bottle	Team bath	Trainer's bucket	Plastic cup

goal

FINAL SCORE

		V		**0**

[ ] V [ ]

FOURTH ROUND

Any time is a good time to score in a cup-tie!

Draw the hands on the clock and follow Katie's special day out watching her team.

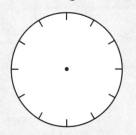

3 o'clock
Match kicks off

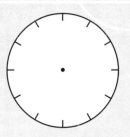

3.10
They score
0–1

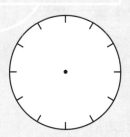

3.20
They score
0–2

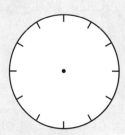

3.30
We score
1–2

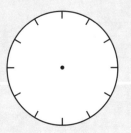

3.40
Disaster! They
score again
1–3

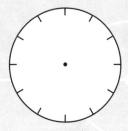

3.45
Half-time

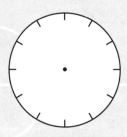

4 o'clock
Second half
kicks off

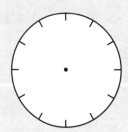

4.15
We score
2–3

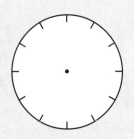

4.20
We equalise
3–3

4.30
We take
the lead
4–3

4.40
They miss
a penalty

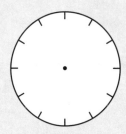

4.50
Full-time
We win 4–3
*A day to
remember!*

goal

FINAL SCORE

[ ] V [ ] 0

	V	

No problem. Get all your shots on target!

1 Each boot has 6 studs.

1 boot has 1 set of 6 studs	1 × 6 = 6
2 boots have 2 sets of 6 studs	2 × 6 = ____
3 boots have 3 sets of 6 studs	3 × ____ = ____
4 boots have 4 sets of 6 studs	____ × ____ = ____
5 boots have 5 sets of ____ studs	____ × ____ = ____
6 boots have ____ sets of ____ studs	____ × ____ = ____
7 boots have ____ sets of ____ studs	____ × ____ = ____
8 boots have ____ sets of ____ studs	____ × ____ = ____
9 boots have ____ sets of ____ studs	____ × ____ = ____
10 boots have ____ sets of ____ studs	____ × ____ = ____

goal

2 Count in 6's up to 60.

6 → 12 → ☐ → ☐ → ☐ → ☐ → ☐ → ☐ → ☐ → 60

goal

FINAL SCORE

		V		1

16

[   ] V [   ]

LEAGUE

Keep passing until you see the chance to score.

1 Count in 6's again and fill in the gaps.

3 → 9 → [ ] → [ ] → [ ] → [ ] → [ ] → [ ] → [ ] → 57

goal

2 Find and colour a route to goal by counting up in 6's each time. You can only travel in the direction of the arrows and you must go up by 6 each time.

(60)

(54) ← (48) ← (42) ← (36) ← (54) ← (54) ← (54) ← (48)

(36) → (30) → (42) → (36) → (48) → (48) → (48) → (42)

(30) ← (30) ← (36) ← (30) ← (36) ← (48) ← (36) ← (36)

(24) → (30) → (36) → (42) → (24) → (30) → (30) → (30)

(18) ← (24) ← (18) ← (24) ← (18) ← (24) ← (36) ← (24)

(12) → (18) → (12) → (12) → (12) → (12) → (12) → (12)

(6) ← (6) ← (6) ← (6) ← (12) ← (12) ← (6) ← (6)

START

goal

FINAL SCORE

[   ] **1** V [   ]

17

LEAGUE

Fill in your team names

[   ] V [   ]

They're down to ten men. Make your extra man count!

Who has played more games,
and by how many?

| 584 games | 369 games |
| Bob | Neil |

```
  5 8 4
− 3 6 9
─────────
  2 1 5
```
Bob played 215 games more than Neil.

1

For each pair of players work out who has played more games,
and by how many.

| 481 games | 219 games |
| Mark | Simon |

_____ has played _____ more games.

| 218 games | 453 games |
| David | Greg |

_____ has played _____ more games.

| 191 games | 324 games |
| Matt | James |

_____ has played _____ more games.

| 535 games | 241 games |
| Brett | Tim |

_____ has played _____ more games.

| 147 games | 331 games |
| John | Martin |

_____ has played _____ more games.

| 421 games | 187 games |
| Andrew | Nick |

_____ has played _____ more games.

goal

FINAL SCORE

[   ] V [   ] **0**

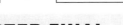

QUARTER-FINAL

Keep trying for the full ninety minutes!

You look at your watch and it is 2.20 p.m.

If the match kicks off at 3.00 p.m., how long is there to kick-off?

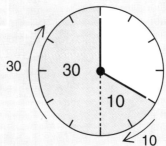

There are 40 minutes to kick-off.

For these times work out how many minutes there are to go until the 3 o'clock kick-off.

_____ minutes   _____ minutes   _____ minutes   _____ minutes

_____ minutes   _____ minutes   _____ minutes   _____ minutes

2:27   2:46   2:33   2:19

_____ minutes   _____ minutes   _____ minutes   _____ minutes

goal

FINAL SCORE

0   V

	V	

Spell it out to your team. They can't lose this one!

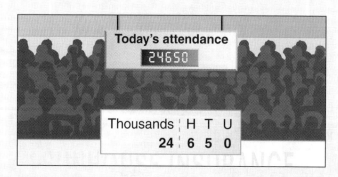

The attendance in words is twenty-four thousand six hundred and fifty. (Watch the hyphens!)

Write these attendances in words in the chart below.

Leeds	Wimbledon	Liverpool
26200	18600	43210

Newcastle	West Ham	Chelsea
34590	19876	25023

Team	Attendance in words

Which team had the highest attendance?_____

Which team had the lowest attendance?_____

goal

FINAL SCORE

	V		0

Fill in your team names

	V	

Minutes are ticking away. Keep going to the final whistle!

Your team score after 78 minutes.

How many minutes are left?

(Football matches are 90 minutes long.)

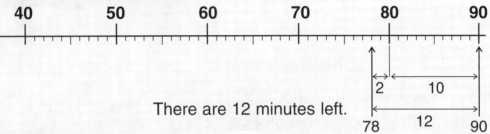

There are 12 minutes left.

1 How many minutes are left in these matches?

 _____ minutes

 _____ minutes

 _____ minutes

 _____ minutes

 _____ minutes

 _____ minutes

 _____ minutes

 _____ minutes

 _____ minutes

goal

FINAL SCORE

	V	
0		

21

[   ] V [   ]

You're the best bar none. Go and prove it!

1

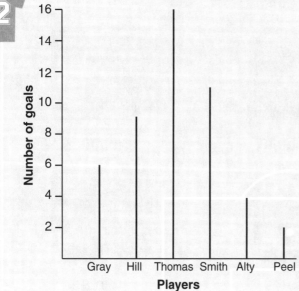

Number of trophies won

Newcastle	3
Tottenham	13
Liverpool	20
Villa	15
Everton	7

Which team has won the most trophies? _____

Which team has won the least trophies? _____

How many trophies have Everton won? _____

How many trophies have Villa won? _____

How many more trophies have Tottenham won than Newcastle? _____

How many trophies have these 5 teams won altogether? _____

goal

2

Goals scored

How many goals did Hill score? ___

How many goals did Thomas score? ___

Who scored 4 goals? _____

Who scored the most goals? _____

How many more goals did Smith score than Peel? ___

Did Thomas score more goals than Gray and Hill together? ___

goal

FINAL SCORE

[|] V [| 1]

Fill in your team names

[   ] **V** [   ]

Still looking good and on course for honours!

1

This pictogram shows the favourite football teams of a group of pupils.

Bolton	👤 👤
West Ham	👤 👤 👤
Tottenham	👤 👤 👤 👤 👤
Sheffield	👤 ⌇
Liverpool	👤 👤 ⌇

key 👤 = 10 votes
⌇ = 5 votes

Bolton received 20 votes.   Sheffield received _____ votes.

West Ham received _____ votes.   Liverpool received _____ votes.

Tottenham received _____ votes.

goal

2

This pictogram shows the goals scored by 5 teams.

Blackburn	○ ○ ○
Newcastle	○ ○ ○ ○ ○ ○
Chelsea	○ ◖
Leeds	○ ○ ○ ○ ◖
Derby	○ ◿

key ○ = 4 goals
◖ = 2 goals
◿ = 1 goal

Blackburn scored _____ goals.   Leeds scored _____ goals.

Newcastle scored _____ goals.   Derby scored _____ goals.

Chelsea scored _____ goals.

goal

FINAL SCORE

[   ] **1** **V** [   ]

V

Turn the tables on the opposition!

This is a multiplication grid.

*	1	2	3	4	5	6
1	1	2	3	4	5	6
2	2	4	6	8	10	12
3	3	6	9	12	15	18
4	4	8	12	16	20	24
5	5	10	15	20	25	30
6	6	12	18	24	30	36

To work out 3×4 you simply look across from 3 and down from 4 to give the answer of 12.

1 First work out these sums in your head, then use the grid above to check your answers.

$2 \times 3 =$ _____ $3 \times 5 =$ _____ $1 \times 5 =$ _____

$4 \times 2 =$ _____ $4 \times 6 =$ _____ $3 \times 2 =$ _____

$5 \times 2 =$ _____ $4 \times 5 =$ _____ $6 \times 2 =$ _____

$3 \times 6 =$ _____ $6 \times 5 =$ _____ $3 \times 6 =$ _____

$2 \times 4 =$ _____ $5 \times 5 =$ _____ $6 \times 4 =$ _____

goal

FINAL SCORE

V

0

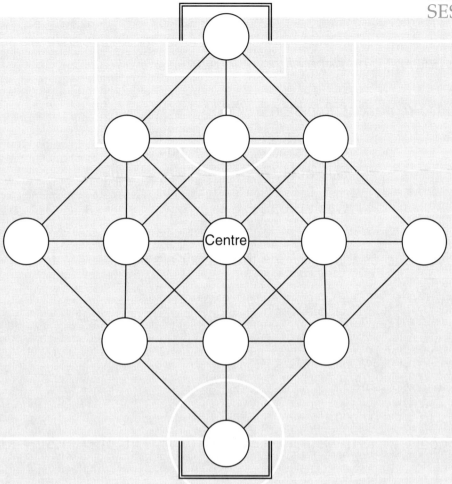

Two players choose their teams and their goals.

Find a counter to use as the ball. The ball starts off at the centre.

Both players roll 2 dice and then multiply their scores together, using the multiplication grid opposite if they want to.

The player with the higher score moves the counter one place in any direction. If both get the same score, throw again.

If a player rolls double six then he/she may move the counter 2 places in any direction.

When a goal is scored the ball returns to the centre.

Fill in your team names

[   ] V [   ]

Plot their downfall and hope all goes to plan!

Co-ordinates represent points on a grid.

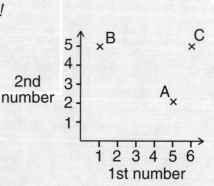

A is at (5,2)

B is at (1,5)

C is at (6,5)

2nd number

1st number

Here is a route to goal that avoids the defenders 👤.

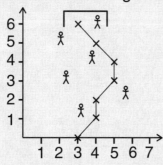

Route to goal   (3,0) → (4,1) → (4,2) → (5,3) → (5,4) → (4,5) → (3,6)

↑
Start

↑
Goal

Write down these routes to goal.

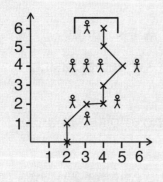

 (2,0) → (2,1) → (   ) → (   ) → (   ) → (   ) → (   ) → (   )

 (6,0) → (   ) → (   ) → (   ) → (   ) → (   ) → (   )

goal

goal

FINAL SCORE

[   ] **1** V [   ]

26

V

Your last league match. Give their defence the run around!

Find your own routes to goal avoiding the defenders 🕴 .

You can only move one dot at a time either up, across or diagonally.

There are many possible answers.

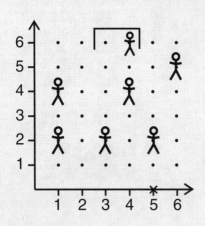

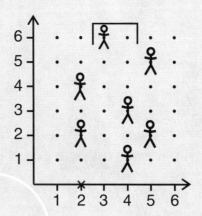

Route 1 (5,0) → (   ) →

Route 2 (2,0) → (   ) →

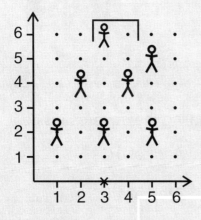

Route 3 (3,0) → (   ) →

Route 4 (4,0) → (   ) →

goal

FINAL SCORE

V   0

	V	

SEMI-FINAL

Next stop Wembley for the winner!

The groundsman marks 12 areas that need reseeding.

Each little square represents a metre square. ☐ = 1 m²

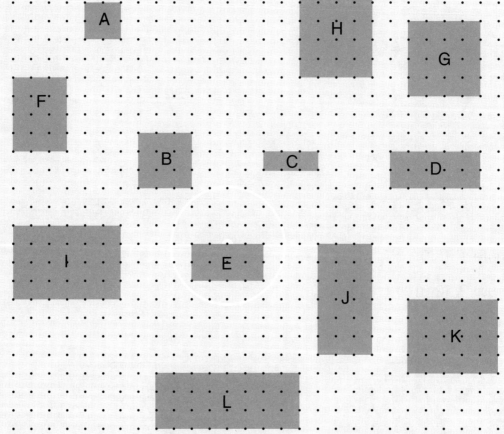
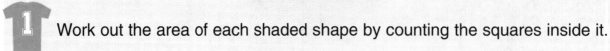

Work out the area of each shaded shape by counting the squares inside it.

Area of A = _____ Area of B = _____ Area of C = _____

Area of D = _____ Area of E = _____ Area of F = _____

Area of G = _____ Area of H = _____ Area of I = _____

Area of J = _____ Area of K = _____ Area of L = _____

goal

FINAL SCORE

	V		0

	V	

FINAL

Congratulations – you've arrived at the twin towers! Enjoy it.

1 Complete these symmetrical tops.

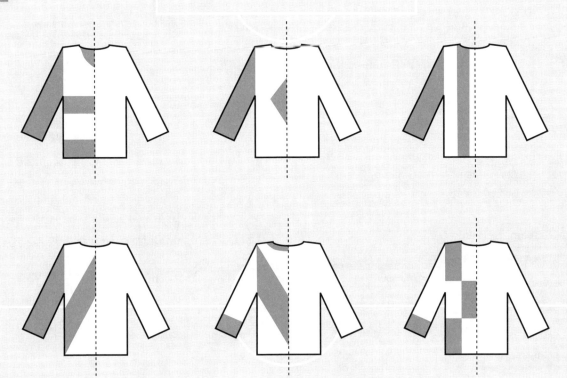

goal

2 Design your own symmetrical tops.

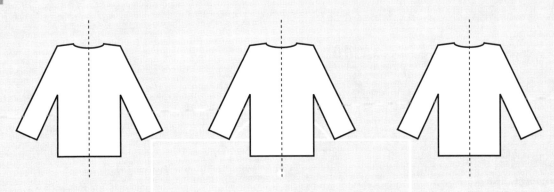

goal

FINAL SCORE

	V		0

29

ANSWERS

The referee's decision is final!

PAGE 4

1 £30, £42, £48

Two or more correct answers scores a goal.

2   £52,
£33,   £47,
£61

Three or more correct answers scores a goal.

PAGE 5

1 Liverpool 22, West Ham 27,
Leeds 15, Newcastle 25,
United 18, Derby 21, Chelsea 19

Five or more correct answers scores a goal.

2

Position	Team	Points
1	West Ham	27
2	Newcastle	25
3	Liverpool	22
4	Derby	21
5	Chelsea	19
6	United	18
7	Leeds	15
8	City	13

Six or more correct answers scores a goal.

PAGE 6

1
$2 \times 3 = \underline{6}$ $7 \times 3 = \underline{21}$
$3 \times 3 = \underline{9}$ $8 \times 3 = \underline{24}$
$4 \times 3 = \underline{12}$ $9 \times 3 = \underline{27}$
$5 \times 3 = \underline{15}$ $10 \times 3 = \underline{30}$
$6 \times 3 = \underline{18}$

Six or more correct answers scores a goal.

2 6 → 9 → 12 → 15 → 18 → 21 → 24 → 27

Five or more correct answers scores a goal.

3 Blackburn 18, Tottenham 9,
Liverpool 21, Leeds 30,
Southampton 15, Derby 6,
Chelsea 12, West Ham 24, Bolton 27

Six or more correct answers scores a goal.

PAGE 8

1 Dave 212, Tom 324, Daniel 442,
Richard 342, Henry 576, Sam 454

Four or more correct answers scores a goal.

PAGE 9

1

Square   Triangle
Rectangle   Circle
Pentagon   Hexagon
Parallelogram Rhombus

Six or more correct answers scores a goal.

2

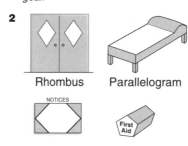

Rhombus   Parallelogram

Hexagon   Pentagon

Three or more correct answers scores a goal.

PAGE 10

1

Dave — Chips 81, Can 62, Total 143
Steve — Chips 81, Apple pie 93, Total 174
Cath — Nuggets 139, Milk shake 134, Total 273
Jessica — Pizza 195, Milk shake 134, Total 329
Frank — Kebab 182, Milk shake 134, Total 316
John — Burger 174, Ice cream 90, Total 264
Sophie — Pizza 195, Chips 81, Can 62, Total 338
Vicky — Chips 81, Fish 153, Ice cream 90, Total 324
Tom — Burger 174, Apple pie 93, Can 62, Total 329

Six or more correct answers scores a goal.

PAGE 11

1 Ball–grams, Throw–metres,
Game–hours and minutes,
Grass–milligrams, Pitch–metres,
Kick–metres, Cup–millilitres,
Coach–tonnes, Bath–litres.

Six or more correct answers scores a goal.

PAGE 12

1
$3 \times 4 = \underline{12}$ $7 \times 4 = \underline{28}$
$4 \times 4 = \underline{16}$ $8 \times 4 = \underline{32}$
$5 \times 4 = \underline{20}$ $9 \times 4 = \underline{36}$
$6 \times 4 = \underline{24}$ $10 \times 4 = \underline{40}$

Five or more correct answers scores a goal.

2 12 → 16 → 20 → 24 → 28 → 32 → 36

Five or more correct answers scores a goal.

PAGE 13

1 10 → 14 → 18 → 22 → 26 → 30 → 34

Five or more correct answers scores a goal.

2

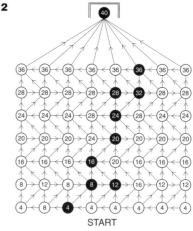

START

Seven or more correct answers scores a goal.

PAGE 14

1 Programme 100 g, Player 85 kg,
Ball 400 g, Team coach 12 tonnes,
Ball boy 30 kg

Three or more correct answers scores a goal.

2 Can 300 ml, Drink bottle 750 ml, Team bath 15 000 litres, Trainer's bucket 10 litres, Plastic cup 150 ml

Three or more correct answers scores a goal.

▶ PAGE **15**

1

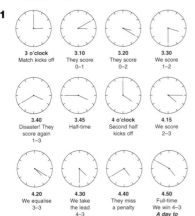

3 o'clock Match kicks off	**3.10** They score 0–1
3.20 They score 0–2	**3.30** We score 1–2
3.40 Disaster! They score again 1–3	**3.45** Half-time
4 o'clock Second half kicks off	**4.15** We score 2–3
4.20 We equalise 3–3	**4.30** We take the lead 4–3
4.40 They miss a penalty	**4.50** Full-time We win 4–3 *A day to remember!*

Eight or more correct answers scores a goal.

▶ PAGE **16**

1
$2 \times 6 = \underline{12}$ $7 \times 6 = \underline{42}$
$3 \times 6 = \underline{18}$ $8 \times 6 = \underline{48}$
$4 \times 6 = \underline{24}$ $9 \times 6 = \underline{54}$
$5 \times 6 = \underline{30}$ $10 \times 6 = \underline{60}$
$6 \times 6 = \underline{36}$

Six or more correct answers scores a goal.

2 18 → 24 → 30 → 36 → 42 → 48 → 54

Five or more correct answers scores a goal.

▶ PAGE **17**

1 15 → 21 → 27 → 33 → 39 → 45 → 51

Five or more correct answers scores a goal.

2
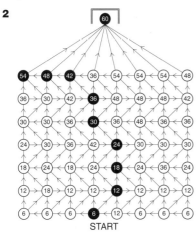
START

Seven or more correct answers scores a goal.

▶ PAGE **18**

1 Mark 262, Greg 235, James 133, Brett 294, Martin 184, Andrew 234

Four or more correct answers scores a goal.

▶ PAGE **19**

1

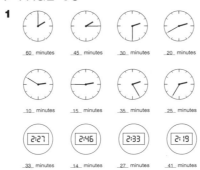

_60_ minutes   _45_ minutes   _30_ minutes   _20_ minutes

_10_ minutes   _15_ minutes   _35_ minutes   _25_ minutes

2:27   2:46   2:33   2:19

_33_ minutes   _14_ minutes   _27_ minutes   _41_ minutes

Eight or more correct answers scores a goal.

▶ PAGE **20**

1

Team	Attendance in words
Leeds	twenty-six thousand two hundred
Wimbledon	eighteen thousand six hundred
Liverpool	forty-three thousand two hundred and ten
Newcastle	thirty-four thousand five hundred and ninety
West Ham	nineteen thousand eight hundred and seventy-six
Chelsea	twenty-five thousand and twenty-three

Liverpool highest, Wimbledon lowest

Six or more correct answers scores a goal.

▶ PAGE **21**

1
60.00   85.00   72.00
_30_ minutes   _5_ minutes   _18_ minutes

48.00   53.00   64.00
_42_ minutes   _37_ minutes   _26_ minutes

59.00   68.00   46.00
_31_ minutes   _22_ minutes   _44_ minutes

Six or more correct answers scores a goal.

▶ PAGE **22**

1 Liverpool most, Newcastle least, Everton 7, Villa 15, 10 more, 58 altogether

Four or more correct answers scores a goal.

2 Hill 9, Thomas 16, Alty, Thomas, 9 more, yes

Four or more correct answers scores a goal.

▶ PAGE **23**

1 West Ham 30, Tottenham 60 Sheffield 15, Liverpool 25,

Three or more correct answers scores a goal.

2 Blackburn 12, Newcastle 24, Chelsea 6, Leeds 18, Derby 5

$2 \times 3 = \underline{6}$ $3 \times 5 = \underline{15}$ $1 \times 5 = \underline{5}$

Three or more correct answers scores a goal.

$2 \times 5 = \underline{10}$ $4 \times 5 = \underline{20}$ $6 \times 2 = \underline{12}$

▶ PAGE **24**

$5 \times 4 = \underline{20}$ $6 \times 5 = \underline{30}$ $3 \times 6 = \underline{18}$

1 $2 \times 4 = \underline{8}$ $5 \times 5 = \underline{25}$ $6 \times 4 = \underline{24}$

Ten or more correct answers scores a goal.

▶ PAGE **26**

1 (3,2) → (4,2) → (4,3) → (5,4) → (4,5) → (4,6)

Four or more correct answers scores a goal.

2 (6,1) → (5,2) → (4,3) → (4,4) → (3,5) → (3,6)

Four or more correct answers scores a goal.

▶ PAGE **27**

1 Many possible routes.

Three or more correct answers scores a goal.

▶ PAGE **28**

1 A = 4 m², B = 9 m², C = 3 m², D = 10 m², E = 8 m², F = 12 m², G = 16 m², H = 20 m², I = 24 m², J = 18 m², K = 20 m², L = 24 m²

Eight or more correct answers scores a goal.

▶ PAGE **29**

1

Four or more correct answers scores a goal.

2 Many possible patterns.

Two or more correct answers scores a goal.

Bobby Charlton Soccer Schools
'Learning through Football'

Special School courses are available at the Bobby Charlton Soccer School HQ in Manchester throughout the year, either residentially or non residential. All participants will be able to tackle the problems of Key Stage 2 Maths and English, as well as receive expert tuition putting them through their soccer paces. There will also be an opportunity to visit the great Manchester attractions of Manchester United FC and Granada Tours. For further details contact John Shiels at Bobby Charlton Sports School, Hopwood Hall, Rochdale Road, Middleton, Manchester, M24 6XH or Telephone: 0161 643 3113 Fax: 0161 643 1444.

Individual courses in Maths and football are available each Easter vacation.

Oxford University Press, Great Clarendon Street, Oxford OX2 6DP

Oxford New York
Athens Auckland Bangkok Bogota Bombay Buenos Aires
Calcutta Cape Town Dar es Salaam Delhi
Florence Hong Kong Istanbul Karachi
Kuala Lumpur Madras Madrid Melbourne
Mexico City Nairobi Paris Singapore
Taipei Tokyo Toronto Warsaw

and associated companies in
Berlin Ibadan

Oxford is a trade mark of Oxford University Press

© Oxford University Press 1998
First published 1998

ISBN 019 838224 3

Typeset and designed by Oxprint Design, Oxford

Printed in Hong Kong